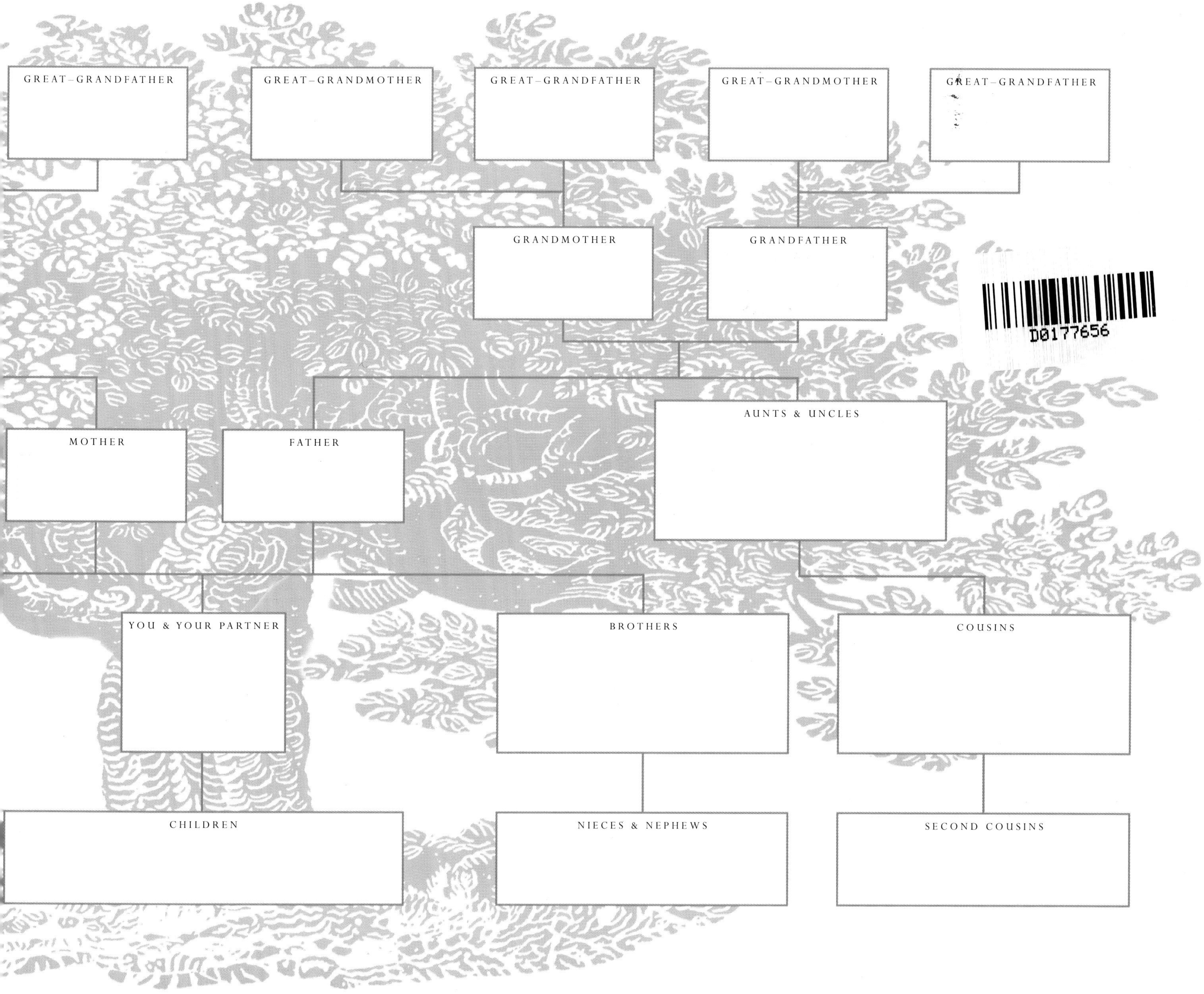
GREAT–GRANDFATHER
GREAT–GRANDMOTHER
GREAT–GRANDFATHER
GREAT–GRANDMOTHER
GREAT–GRANDFATHER
GRANDMOTHER
GRANDFATHER
AUNTS & UNCLES
MOTHER
FATHER
YOU & YOUR PARTNER
BROTHERS
COUSINS
CHILDREN
NIECES & NEPHEWS
SECOND COUSINS

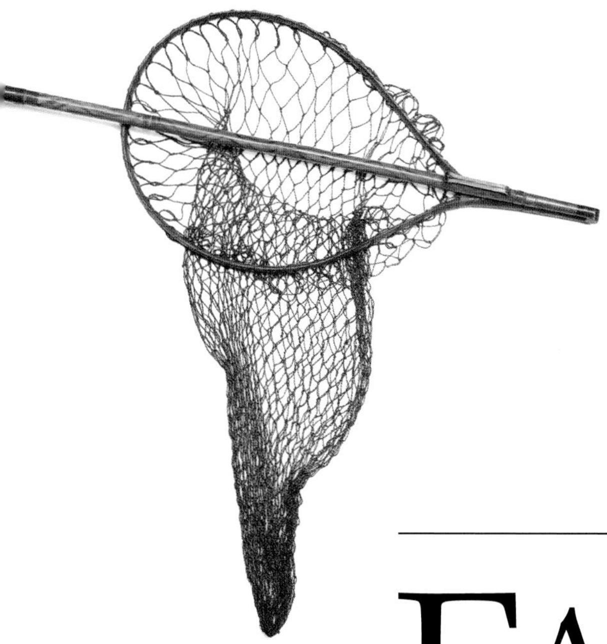

OUR FAMILY TREE RECORD BOOK

DORLING KINDERSLEY
LONDON • NEW YORK • SYDNEY • MOSCOW

A DORLING KINDERSLEY BOOK

Design and text Mason Linklater

Managing Art Editor Philip Gilderdale
Managing Editor Jemima Dunne
Senior Art Editor Karen Ward
Production Antony Heller

Special photography David Merewether
Border illustration Jane Thomson

First published in Great Britain in 1997 by
Dorling Kindersley Limited,
9 Henrietta Street, London WC2E 8PS
4 6 8 10 9 7 5 3
Visit us on the World Wide Web at
http://www.dk.com

A CIP catalogue record for this book is available from the British Library

ISBN 0-7513-0474-3

Colour reproduction by Colorlito Rigogliosi S.R.L., Milan, Italy
Printed and bound by Tien Wah Press, Singapore

ACKNOWLEDGMENTS

Dorling Kindersley would like to thank the following for their kind assistance in supplying items for special photography: Gunvor Avery and Ingrid Mason.

The following photographs were reproduced by courtesy of London Toy and Model Museum, pages 12, 22, 29; Mattel UK Ltd., page 13; Faith Eaton Collection, pages 22, 40, 55; Worthing Museum and Art Gallery, page 24; Judy Sparrow, page 28; Lawleys Ltd., page 37; Paul and Rosemary Volpp, page 46; National Maritime Museum, page 47.

Contents

You & Your Family

Your Partner's Family

TRACING YOUR FAMILY TREE

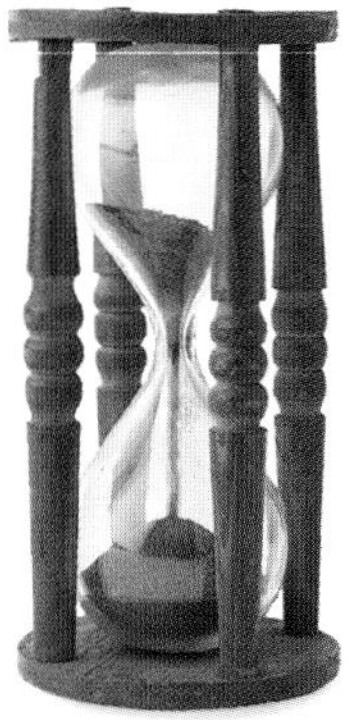

Where would we be without our families and the life we enjoy with them? Family gives us stability and reassurance in a world of rapid change. It applauds our triumphs and achievements without envy, bears with us when times are hard, and is the mainstay in celebrating landmark events throughout our lives. Family is about continuity, knowing where we have come from and seeing where we are going. Every family has its unique characteristics – whether of intellect, looks, or temperament – that pass from one generation to the next. When we look into the past, we see members of our family mirrored in generations gone by (Mum has her father's eyes; Dad has Grandma's amazing memory); when we observe the present and look forward into the future, we see ourselves reflected in our children.

Setting out on your search

In constructing a family tree, a skilful, seasoned genealogist is able to trace the direct line of descent through many generations, covering hundreds of years with probably thousands of names. Such a search is not only time-consuming but also costly; as an alternative, you can set out on your search with the more modest and achievable aim of compiling the family tree (or "pedigree", as it is known) of your most recent ancestors. Cataloguing the accumulated knowledge of your parents should enable you to trace your family tree back as far as your great-grandparents' generation, on both your mother's and your father's side. In the process, you may even turn up long-lost or far-flung relatives who will provide vital clues for research into more distant times.

Sources of information: family stories & papers

First decide whether to trace your maternal and paternal lines at the same time. Tracing both lines simultaneously will not affect the result, but you may find it less complicated to complete your research into one line before starting on the other. Let every family member know that you are researching your family tree, and enlist their help to provide as much information as possible, especially details of marriages, which will be recorded, and other longstanding liaisons, which may not be documented except in personal reminiscences. Sketch out a rough family tree that shows each generation on a separate level, and keep in a series of notebooks or computer files a meticulous record of every piece of evidence you discover. Plan on updating these – and your sketch – regularly as new

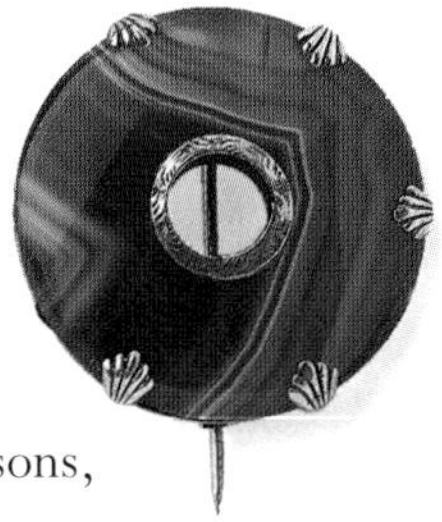

information emerges, and do not destroy any evidence until you are sure it has no relevance. Visit elderly relatives in person, and tape your conversations with them to transcribe and refer to later. Never forget the importance of family correspondence and diaries, which often turn up surprising information (for example, details of illegitimate children or divorces) that sensitive relatives may be unwilling to reveal.

Matters of public record

Occasionally, you may need to test the accuracy of information sourced from family members, in particular elderly ones; or perhaps some line of enquiry will prove inconclusive. This is the time to consider moving on to a more serious level of research: consulting public records. Certificates of birth and marriage are your starting point, and although details vary from one region and time period to another, the basic information is the same. A birth certificate records the individual's name, parents (including the mother's maiden name and the father's occupation), and the date and place of birth. A marriage certificate shows the names of the couple (and their fathers' names), residence and age when married, and the date and place of the ceremony. Wills, census reports, and parochial and civil records also yield useful information. For this level of research, it is well worth joining your local historical or genealogical society, which can guide you through the complicated maze of the public record system.

An heirloom for future generations

Taking time to trace your family tree is an opportunity to gather your own treasury of remembrance, memento, and fact. You will probably find that you become more and more engrossed in your searches as you discover new leads, pursuing them from one part of the country to another (even to other continents) to bring together all the rich detail of your family's history and your partner's.

As your quest reveals each new name, write it in your notebook and then go on with your research. Remember, especially if your surname is not unusual, that a name must be verified with biographical detail that clearly identifies that person as a member of your family. Only then can you record the name on the family tree at the front or back of this book.

The detective work involved in tracing your family tree is its own reward, yet small when compared with the satisfaction of getting to know your family by means of undiscovered legend, quirky anecdote, and buried secret. So always be on the lookout for new tales to increase your collection. Trivial yet fascinating, such details bring your family tree to life, and transform it into a unique heirloom for future generations.

ALL ABOUT YOU

Significant details

NAME & NICKNAMES

DATE, PLACE & TIME OF BIRTH

DISTINGUISHING PHYSICAL FEATURES

TYPICAL FAMILY CHARACTERISTICS

CLOSEST FRIENDS OR CONFIDANTES

PHOTOGRAPH

Childhood

CHILDHOOD HOME

EARLIEST MEMORY OF MOTHER & FATHER

MOST & LEAST LIKED FOODS

FAVOURITE GAMES & TOYS

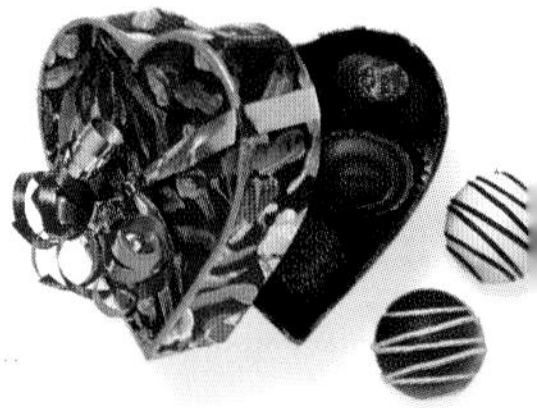

BEST FRIENDS

FAMILY PETS

FIRST SCHOOL

Teenage years

SECOND SCHOOL

FAVOURITE LESSONS & TEACHERS

SPECIAL FRIENDS

FAVOURITE HOBBIES & PASTIMES

FIRST DATE

FAVOURITE SINGER OR GROUP & SONG

Adulthood

FURTHER EDUCATION

FIRST JOB

FIRST PAY PACKET

FIRST HOME OF YOUR OWN

FAVOURITE LEISURE ACTIVITIES

FAVOURITE HOLIDAYS & DESTINATIONS

MAJOR ACHIEVEMENTS & AMBITIONS

ALL ABOUT YOUR PARTNER

Significant details

NAME & NICKNAMES

DATE, PLACE & TIME OF BIRTH

DISTINGUISHING PHYSICAL FEATURES

TYPICAL FAMILY CHARACTERISTICS

CLOSEST FRIENDS OR CONFIDANTES

PHOTOGRAPH

Childhood

CHILDHOOD HOME

EARLIEST MEMORY OF MOTHER & FATHER

MOST & LEAST LIKED FOODS

FAVOURITE GAMES & TOYS

BEST FRIENDS

FAMILY PETS

FIRST SCHOOL

Teenage years

SECOND SCHOOL

FAVOURITE LESSONS & TEACHERS

SPECIAL FRIENDS

FAVOURITE HOBBIES & PASTIMES

FIRST DATE

FAVOURITE SINGER OR GROUP & SONG

Adulthood

FURTHER EDUCATION

FIRST JOB

FIRST PAY PACKET

FIRST OWN HOME

FAVOURITE LEISURE ACTIVITIES

FAVOURITE HOLIDAYS & DESTINATIONS

MAJOR ACHIEVEMENTS & AMBITIONS

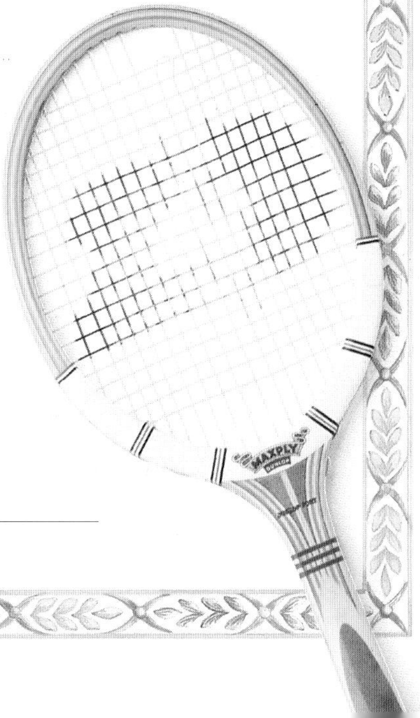

Your Marriage

HOW YOU & YOUR PARTNER FIRST MET

CIRCUMSTANCES OF MARRIAGE PROPOSAL

The wedding

DATE, PLACE & TIME OF CEREMONY

WHAT THE WEATHER WAS LIKE

BEST MAN & USHERS

BRIDESMAIDS, MAIDS OF HONOUR & ATTENDANTS

WEDDING & GOING-AWAY OUTFITS

RECEPTION VENUE, FOOD & DRINK

MEMORABLE MOMENTS OF THE CEREMONY

HONEYMOON MEMORIES

FIRST NIGHT TOGETHER

PHOTOGRAPH

PHOTOGRAPH

Your life together

YOUR FIRST HOME

YOUR HOME NOW

YOUR FIRST MARRIED YEAR

HOPES, DREAMS & AMBITIONS

YOUR FIRST ANNIVERSARY

Your Children

First child

NAME & NICKNAMES

DATE, PLACE & TIME OF BIRTH

SPECIAL MEMORIES OF THE BIRTH

FIRST WORDS

FIRST STEPS

FIRST CHRISTMAS

FIRST DAY AT SCHOOL

Second child

NAME & NICKNAMES

DATE, PLACE & TIME OF BIRTH

SPECIAL MEMORIES OF THE BIRTH

FIRST WORDS

FIRST STEPS

FIRST CHRISTMAS

FIRST DAY AT SCHOOL

PHOTOGRAPH

PHOTOGRAPH

PHOTOGRAPH

Third child

NAME & NICKNAMES

DATE, PLACE & TIME OF BIRTH

SPECIAL MEMORIES OF THE BIRTH

FIRST WORDS

FIRST STEPS

FIRST CHRISTMAS

FIRST DAY AT SCHOOL

Names of other children

YOUR MOTHER

Significant details

NAME & NICKNAMES

DATE, PLACE & TIME OF BIRTH

DISTINGUISHING PHYSICAL FEATURES

TYPICAL FAMILY CHARACTERISTICS

BEST FRIENDS

PHOTOGRAPH

Childhood

CHILDHOOD HOME

SIGNIFICANT MEMORIES OF PARENTS

FAVOURITE GAMES & PASTIMES

FAMILY PETS

MOST SIGNIFICANT CHILDHOOD MEMORY

MEMORIES OF SCHOOL & TEACHERS

Adulthood

FURTHER EDUCATION

FIRST JOB

FIRST PAY PACKET

FIRST MEETING WITH YOUR FATHER

FIRST IMPRESSION OF YOUR FATHER

DATE, PLACE & TIME OF MARRIAGE

HONEYMOON MEMORIES

FIRST HOME TOGETHER

FAVOURITE HOBBIES & PASTIMES

MAJOR AMBITIONS & ACHIEVEMENTS

Her brothers & sisters

NAME

DATE OF BIRTH

CHILDREN

NAME

DATE OF BIRTH

CHILDREN

NAME

DATE OF BIRTH

CHILDREN

NAME

DATE OF BIRTH

CHILDREN

NAMES OF OTHER SIBLINGS

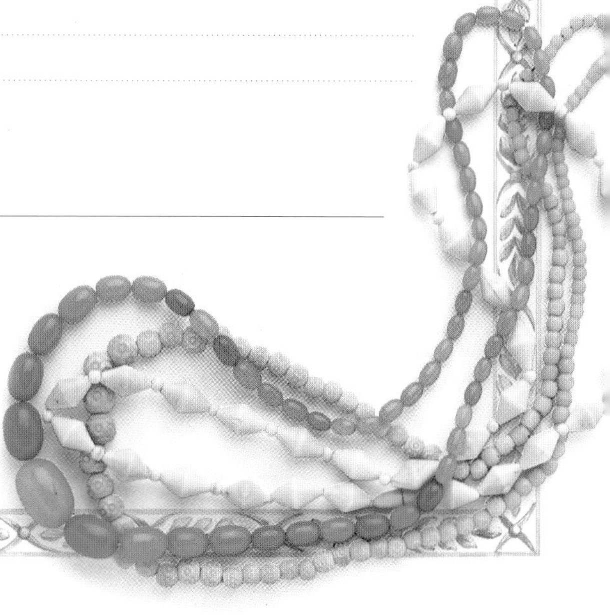

Your Father

Significant details

NAME & NICKNAMES

DATE, PLACE & TIME OF BIRTH

DISTINGUISHING PHYSICAL FEATURES

TYPICAL FAMILY CHARACTERISTICS

BEST FRIENDS

Childhood

CHILDHOOD HOME

SIGNIFICANT MEMORIES OF PARENTS

FAVOURITE GAMES & PASTIMES

FAMILY PETS

MOST SIGNIFICANT CHILDHOOD MEMORY

SPECIAL FRIENDS

MEMORIES OF SCHOOL & TEACHERS

Adulthood

FURTHER EDUCATION

FIRST JOB

FIRST PAY PACKET

WHEN & HOW HE PROPOSED

FIRST IMPRESSION OF YOUR MOTHER

FAVOURITE SPORTS & HOBBIES

FAVOURITE CITY & HOLIDAY

MEMORABLE EVENTS

MAJOR AMBITIONS & ACHIEVEMENTS

PHOTOGRAPH

His brothers & sisters

NAME

DATE OF BIRTH

CHILDREN

NAME

DATE OF BIRTH

CHILDREN

NAME

DATE OF BIRTH

CHILDREN

NAME

DATE OF BIRTH

CHILDREN

NAMES OF OTHER SIBLINGS

YOUR BROTHERS & SISTERS

Brother

NAME & NICKNAMES

DATE OF BIRTH

TYPICAL FAMILY CHARACTERISTICS

SIGNIFICANT CHILDHOOD MEMORIES

PARTNER

HOME

His children

NAMES & NICKNAMES

DATES OF BIRTH

PHOTOGRAPH

PHOTOGRAPH

Brother

NAME & NICKNAMES

DATE OF BIRTH

TYPICAL FAMILY CHARACTERISTICS

SIGNIFICANT CHILDHOOD MEMORIES

PARTNER

HOME

His children

NAMES & NICKNAMES

DATES OF BIRTH

Sister

NAME & NICKNAMES

DATE OF BIRTH

TYPICAL FAMILY CHARACTERISTICS

SIGNIFICANT CHILDHOOD MEMORIES

PARTNER

HOME

PHOTOGRAPH

Sister

NAME & NICKNAMES

DATE OF BIRTH

TYPICAL FAMILY CHARACTERISTICS

SIGNIFICANT CHILDHOOD MEMORIES

PARTNER

HOME

Her children

NAMES & NICKNAMES

DATES OF BIRTH

PHOTOGRAPH

Her children

NAMES & NICKNAMES

DATES OF BIRTH

YOUR OTHER CLOSE RELATIVES

On your Mother's side

NAME & NICKNAMES

DATE OF BIRTH

HOW RELATED

CHILDREN

SPECIAL FAMILY MEMORIES

NAME & NICKNAMES

DATE OF BIRTH

HOW RELATED

CHILDREN

SPECIAL FAMILY MEMORIES

PHOTOGRAPH

NAME & NICKNAMES

DATE OF BIRTH

HOW RELATED

CHILDREN

SPECIAL FAMILY MEMORIES

NAME & NICKNAMES

DATE OF BIRTH

HOW RELATED

CHILDREN

SPECIAL FAMILY MEMORIES

On your Father's side

NAME & NICKNAMES

DATE OF BIRTH

HOW RELATED

CHILDREN

SPECIAL FAMILY MEMORIES

NAME & NICKNAMES

DATE OF BIRTH

HOW RELATED

CHILDREN

SPECIAL FAMILY MEMORIES

PHOTOGRAPH

NAME & NICKNAMES

DATE OF BIRTH

HOW RELATED

CHILDREN

SPECIAL FAMILY MEMORIES

NAME & NICKNAMES

DATE OF BIRTH

HOW RELATED

CHILDREN

SPECIAL FAMILY MEMORIES

YOUR MATERNAL GRANDMOTHER

Significant details

NAME & NICKNAMES

DATE & PLACE OF BIRTH

DISTINGUISHING PHYSICAL FEATURES

PHOTOGRAPH

TYPICAL FAMILY CHARACTERISTICS

Childhood

CHILDHOOD HOME

FAVOURITE ACTIVITIES

MEMORIES OF PARENTS

MEMORIES OF SCHOOL

Adulthood

FURTHER EDUCATION

FIRST JOB

FIRST PAY PACKET

FIRST MEETING WITH YOUR GRANDFATHER

FIRST IMPRESSION OF YOUR GRANDFATHER

FIRST HOME

FAVOURITE HOBBIES & PASTIMES

MEMORABLE JOURNEYS & EVENTS

Her brothers & sisters

NAME

DATE OF BIRTH

CHILDREN

NAME

DATE OF BIRTH

CHILDREN

NAME

DATE OF BIRTH

CHILDREN

NAME

DATE OF BIRTH

CHILDREN

NAMES OF OTHER SIBLINGS

YOUR MATERNAL GRANDFATHER

Significant details

NAME & NICKNAMES

DATE & PLACE OF BIRTH

DISTINGUISHING PHYSICAL FEATURES

TYPICAL FAMILY CHARACTERISTICS

PHOTOGRAPH

Childhood

CHILDHOOD HOME

FAVOURITE ACTIVITIES

MEMORIES OF PARENTS

MEMORIES OF SCHOOL

Adulthood

FURTHER EDUCATION

FIRST JOB

FIRST PAY PACKET

WHEN & HOW HE PROPOSED

FIRST IMPRESSION OF YOUR GRANDMOTHER

HONEYMOON MEMORIES

GRANDPARENTS' HOME YOU REMEMBER

FAVOURITE HOBBIES & PASTIMES

MEMORABLE JOURNEYS & EVENTS

His brothers & sisters

NAME

DATE OF BIRTH

CHILDREN

NAME

DATE OF BIRTH

CHILDREN

NAME

DATE OF BIRTH

CHILDREN

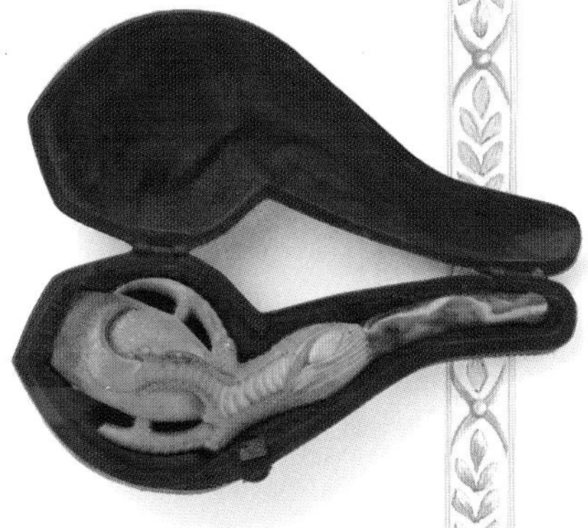

NAME

DATE OF BIRTH

CHILDREN

NAMES OF OTHER SIBLINGS

YOUR PATERNAL GRANDMOTHER

Significant details

NAME & NICKNAMES

DATE & PLACE OF BIRTH

DISTINGUISHING PHYSICAL FEATURES

TYPICAL FAMILY CHARACTERISTICS

PHOTOGRAPH

Childhood

CHILDHOOD HOME

FAVOURITE ACTIVITIES

MEMORIES OF PARENTS

MEMORIES OF SCHOOL

Adulthood

FURTHER EDUCATION

FIRST JOB

FIRST PAY PACKET

FIRST MEETING WITH YOUR GRANDFATHER

FIRST IMPRESSION OF YOUR GRANDFATHER

FIRST HOME

FAVOURITE HOBBIES & PASTIMES

MEMORABLE JOURNEYS & EVENTS

Her brothers & sisters

NAME

DATE OF BIRTH

CHILDREN

NAME

DATE OF BIRTH

CHILDREN

NAME

DATE OF BIRTH

CHILDREN

NAME

DATE OF BIRTH

CHILDREN

NAMES OF OTHER SIBLINGS

Your Paternal Grandfather

Significant details

NAME & NICKNAMES

DATE & PLACE OF BIRTH

DISTINGUISHING PHYSICAL FEATURES

TYPICAL FAMILY CHARACTERISTICS

Childhood

CHILDHOOD HOME

FAVOURITE ACTIVITIES

MEMORIES OF PARENTS

MEMORIES OF SCHOOL

Adulthood

FURTHER EDUCATION

FIRST JOB

FIRST PAY PACKET

WHEN & HOW HE PROPOSED

FIRST IMPRESSION OF YOUR GRANDMOTHER

HONEYMOON MEMORIES

PHOTOGRAPH

GRANDPARENTS' HOME YOU REMEMBER

FAVOURITE HOBBIES & PASTIMES

MEMORABLE TRAVEL

His brothers & sisters

NAME

DATE OF BIRTH

CHILDREN

NAME

DATE OF BIRTH

CHILDREN

NAME

DATE OF BIRTH

CHILDREN

NAME

DATE OF BIRTH

CHILDREN

NAMES OF OTHER SIBLINGS

Your Great-Grandparents

Maternal grandmother's mother

NAME

DATE & PLACE OF BIRTH

WHEN & WHERE MARRIED

PHOTOGRAPH

Maternal grandfather's mother

NAME

DATE & PLACE OF BIRTH

WHEN & WHERE MARRIED

PHOTOGRAPH

Maternal grandmother's father

PHOTOGRAPH

NAME

DATE & PLACE OF BIRTH

HONEYMOON MEMORIES

Maternal grandfather's father

PHOTOGRAPH

NAME

DATE & PLACE OF BIRTH

HONEYMOON MEMORIES

Paternal grandmother's mother

NAME

DATE & PLACE OF BIRTH

PHOTOGRAPH

WHEN & WHERE MARRIED

Paternal grandfather's mother

NAME

DATE & PLACE OF BIRTH

PHOTOGRAPH

WHEN & WHERE MARRIED

Paternal grandmother's father

NAME

PHOTOGRAPH

DATE & PLACE OF BIRTH

HONEYMOON MEMORIES

Paternal grandfather's father

NAME

PHOTOGRAPH

DATE & PLACE OF BIRTH

HONEYMOON MEMORIES

YOUR OTHER ANCESTORS

Mother's ancestors

NAME

DATE & PLACE OF BIRTH

HOW RELATED

DATE OF DEATH

WHERE BURIED

NAME

DATE & PLACE OF BIRTH

HOW RELATED

DATE OF DEATH

WHERE BURIED

PHOTOGRAPH

NAME

DATE & PLACE OF BIRTH

HOW RELATED

DATE OF DEATH

WHERE BURIED

HOW YOU TRACED THEM

STORIES YOU HAVE HEARD ABOUT THEM

CHARACTERISTICS PASSED ON TO YOU

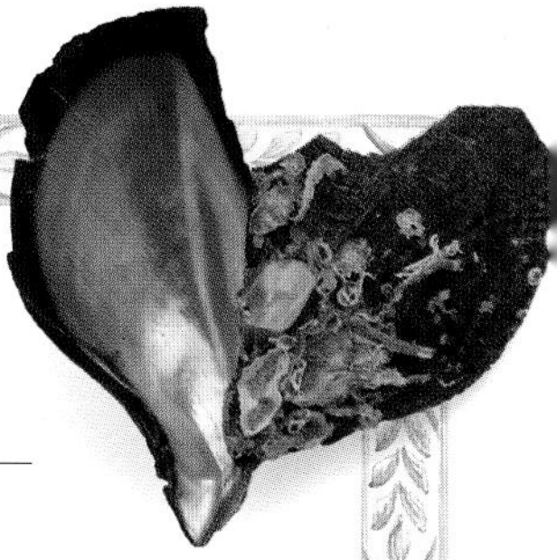

Father's ancestors

NAME

DATE & PLACE OF BIRTH

HOW RELATED

DATE OF DEATH

WHERE BURIED

PHOTOGRAPH

NAME

DATE & PLACE OF BIRTH

HOW RELATED

DATE OF DEATH

WHERE BURIED

NAME

DATE & PLACE OF BIRTH

HOW RELATED

DATE OF DEATH

WHERE BURIED

HOW YOU TRACED THEM

STORIES YOU HAVE HEARD ABOUT THEM

CHARACTERISTICS PASSED ON TO YOU

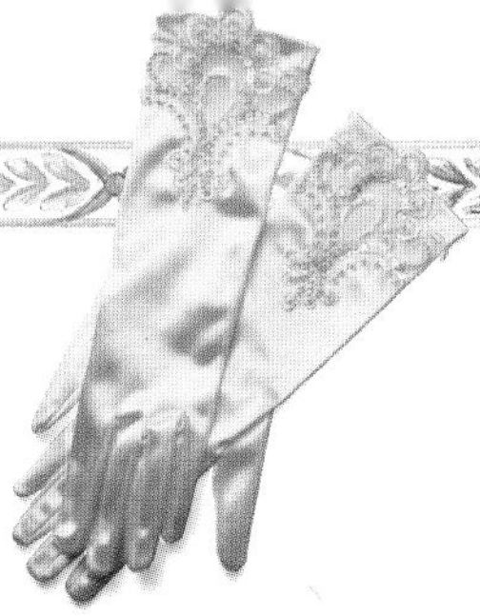

FAMILY STORIES & ANECDOTES

STORIES ABOUT YOU

ANECDOTES ABOUT FAMILY OCCASIONS

STORIES ABOUT YOUR BROTHERS & SISTERS

PHOTOGRAPH

ANECDOTES ABOUT FAMILY HOLIDAYS

ANECDOTES ABOUT FAMILY PETS

PHOTOGRAPH

STORIES YOUR MOTHER TELLS ABOUT YOUR FATHER

STORIES YOUR FATHER TELLS ABOUT YOUR MOTHER

STORIES ABOUT YOUR AUNTS & UNCLES

STORIES ABOUT YOUR GRANDPARENTS

STORIES ABOUT YOUR GREAT–GRANDPARENTS

FAMILY JOKES

YOUR PARTNER'S MOTHER

Significant details

NAME & NICKNAMES

DATE, PLACE & TIME OF BIRTH

DISTINGUISHING PHYSICAL FEATURES

TYPICAL FAMILY CHARACTERISTICS

BEST FRIENDS

PHOTOGRAPH

Childhood

CHILDHOOD HOME

SIGNIFICANT MEMORIES OF PARENTS

FAVOURITE GAMES & PASTIMES

FAMILY PETS

MOST SIGNIFICANT CHILDHOOD MEMORY

SPECIAL FRIENDS

MEMORIES OF SCHOOL & TEACHERS

Adulthood

FURTHER EDUCATION

FIRST JOB

FIRST PAY PACKET

FIRST MEETING WITH YOUR PARTNER'S FATHER

FIRST IMPRESSION OF HIM

DATE, PLACE & TIME OF MARRIAGE

HONEYMOON MEMORIES

FIRST HOME TOGETHER

FAVOURITE HOBBIES & PASTIMES

MAJOR AMBITIONS & ACHIEVEMENTS

Her brothers & sisters

NAME

DATE OF BIRTH

CHILDREN

NAME

DATE OF BIRTH

CHILDREN

NAME

DATE OF BIRTH

CHILDREN

NAME

DATE OF BIRTH

CHILDREN

NAMES OF OTHER SIBLINGS

YOUR PARTNER'S FATHER

Significant details

NAME & NICKNAMES

DATE, PLACE & TIME OF BIRTH

DISTINGUISHING PHYSICAL FEATURES

TYPICAL FAMILY CHARACTERISTICS

PHOTOGRAPH

Childhood

CHILDHOOD HOME

SIGNIFICANT MEMORIES OF PARENTS

FAVOURITE GAMES & PASTIMES

FAMILY PETS

MOST SIGNIFICANT CHILDHOOD MEMORY

SPECIAL FRIENDS

BEST FRIENDS

MEMORIES OF SCHOOL & TEACHERS

Adulthood

FURTHER EDUCATION

FIRST JOB

FIRST PAY PACKET

WHEN & HOW HE PROPOSED

FIRST IMPRESSION OF YOUR PARTNER'S MOTHER

FAVOURITE SPORTS & HOBBIES

FAVOURITE CITY & HOLIDAY

MEMORABLE EVENTS

MAJOR AMBITIONS & ACHIEVEMENTS

His brothers & sisters

NAME

DATE OF BIRTH

CHILDREN

NAME

DATE OF BIRTH

CHILDREN

NAME

DATE OF BIRTH

CHILDREN

NAME

DATE OF BIRTH

CHILDREN

NAMES OF OTHER SIBLINGS

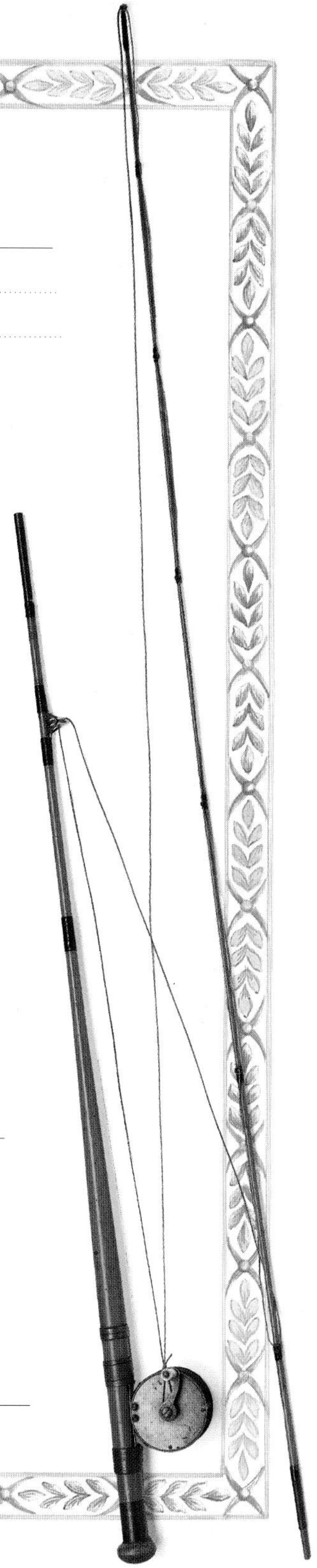

YOUR PARTNER'S BROTHERS & SISTERS

Brother

NAME & NICKNAMES

DATE OF BIRTH

PHOTOGRAPH

TYPICAL FAMILY CHARACTERISTICS

SIGNIFICANT CHILDHOOD MEMORIES

PARTNER

HOME

His children

NAMES & NICKNAMES

DATES OF BIRTH

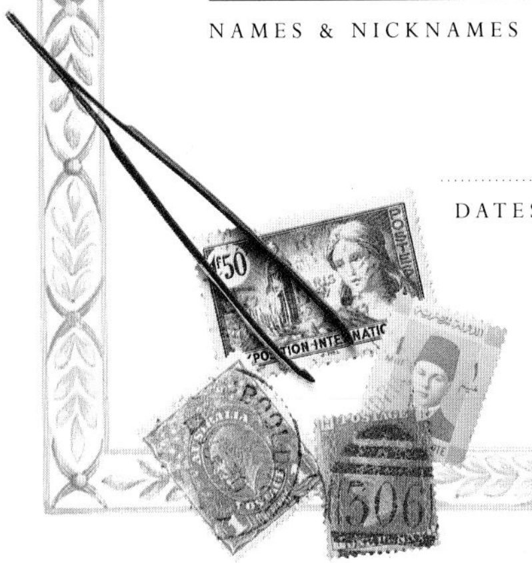

Brother

NAME & NICKNAMES

DATE OF BIRTH

PHOTOGRAPH

TYPICAL FAMILY CHARACTERISTICS

SIGNIFICANT CHILDHOOD MEMORIES

PARTNER

HOME

His children

NAMES & NICKNAMES

DATES OF BIRTH

Sister

NAME & NICKNAMES

PHOTOGRAPH

DATE OF BIRTH

TYPICAL FAMILY CHARACTERISTICS

SIGNIFICANT CHILDHOOD MEMORIES

PARTNER

HOME

Her children

NAMES & NICKNAMES

DATES OF BIRTH

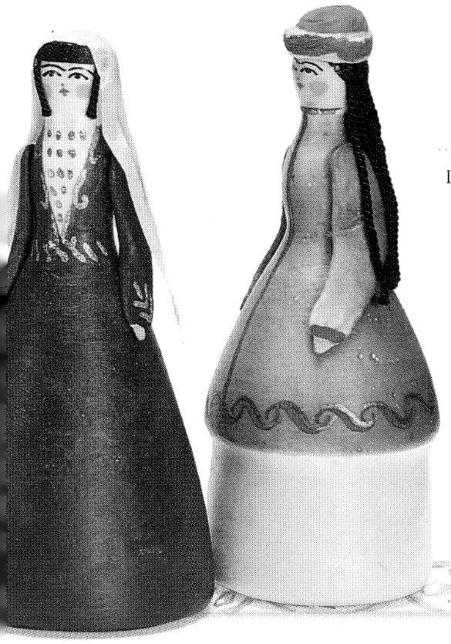

Sister

NAME & NICKNAMES

DATE OF BIRTH

TYPICAL FAMILY CHARACTERISTICS

SIGNIFICANT CHILDHOOD MEMORIES

PARTNER

HOME

PHOTOGRAPH

Her children

NAMES & NICKNAMES

DATES OF BIRTH

YOUR PARTNER'S OTHER CLOSE RELATIVES

On Mother's side

NAME & NICKNAMES

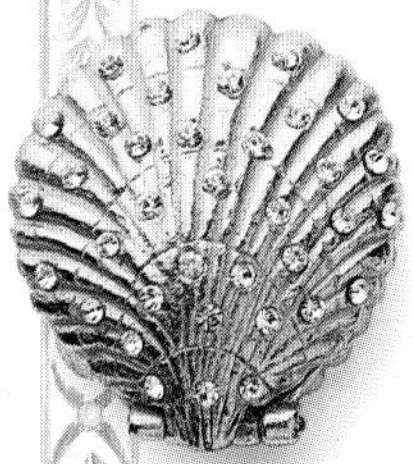

DATE OF BIRTH

HOW RELATED

CHILDREN

SPECIAL FAMILY MEMORIES

PHOTOGRAPH

NAME & NICKNAMES

DATE OF BIRTH

HOW RELATED

CHILDREN

SPECIAL FAMILY MEMORIES

NAME & NICKNAMES

DATE OF BIRTH

HOW RELATED

CHILDREN

SPECIAL FAMILY MEMORIES

PHOTOGRAPH

NAME & NICKNAMES

DATE OF BIRTH

HOW RELATED

CHILDREN

SPECIAL FAMILY MEMORIES

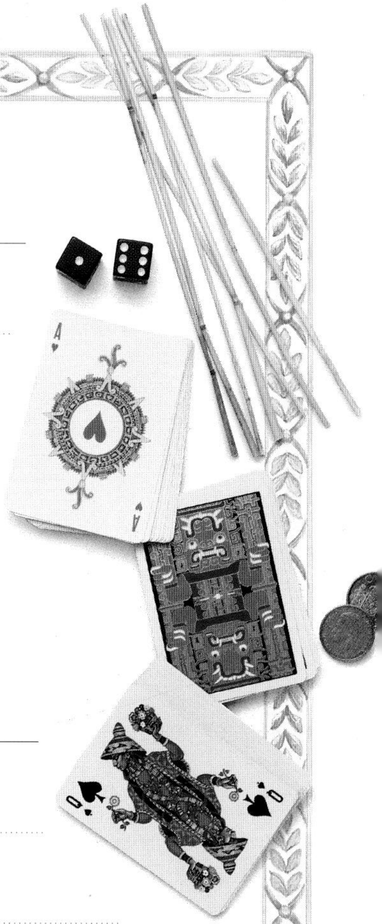

On Father's side

NAME & NICKNAMES

DATE OF BIRTH

HOW RELATED

CHILDREN

SPECIAL FAMILY MEMORIES

NAME & NICKNAMES

DATE OF BIRTH

HOW RELATED

CHILDREN

SPECIAL FAMILY MEMORIES

NAME & NICKNAMES

DATE OF BIRTH

HOW RELATED

CHILDREN

SPECIAL FAMILY MEMORIES

PHOTOGRAPH

NAME & NICKNAMES

DATE OF BIRTH

HOW RELATED

CHILDREN

SPECIAL FAMILY MEMORIES

YOUR PARTNER'S MATERNAL GRANDMOTHER

PHOTOGRAPH

TYPICAL FAMILY CHARACTERISTICS

Childhood

CHILDHOOD HOME

FAVOURITE ACTIVITIES

MEMORIES OF PARENTS

MEMORIES OF SCHOOL

Significant details

NAME & NICKNAMES

DATE & PLACE OF BIRTH

DISTINGUISHING PHYSICAL FEATURES

Adulthood

FURTHER EDUCATION

FIRST JOB

FIRST PAY PACKET

FIRST MEETING WITH YOUR PARTNER'S GRANDFATHER

FIRST IMPRESSION OF HIM

FIRST HOME

FAVOURITE PASTIMES & HOBBIES

MEMORABLE JOURNEYS & EVENTS

Her brothers & sisters

NAME

DATE OF BIRTH

CHILDREN

NAME

DATE OF BIRTH

CHILDREN

NAME

DATE OF BIRTH

CHILDREN

NAME

DATE OF BIRTH

CHILDREN

NAMES OF OTHER SIBLINGS

YOUR PARTNER'S MATERNAL GRANDFATHER

Significant details

NAME & NICKNAMES

DATE & PLACE OF BIRTH

DISTINGUISHING PHYSICAL FEATURES

PHOTOGRAPH

Childhood

CHILDHOOD HOME

FAVOURITE ACTIVITIES

MEMORIES OF PARENTS

TYPICAL FAMILY CHARACTERISTICS

MEMORIES OF SCHOOL

Adulthood

FURTHER EDUCATION

FIRST JOB

FIRST PAY PACKET

WHEN & HOW HE PROPOSED

FIRST IMPRESSION OF YOUR PARTNER'S GRANDMOTHER

HONEYMOON MEMORIES

FAVOURITE HOBBIES & PASTIMES

GRANDPARENTS' HOME YOUR PARTNER REMEMBERS

MEMORABLE JOURNEYS & EVENTS

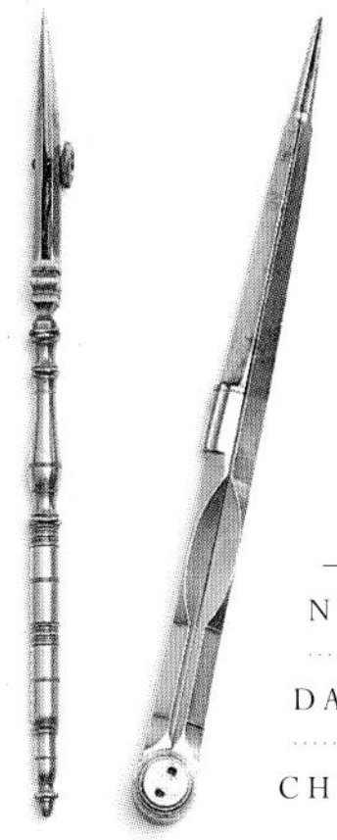

His brothers & sisters

NAME

DATE OF BIRTH

CHILDREN

NAME

DATE OF BIRTH

CHILDREN

NAME

DATE OF BIRTH

CHILDREN

NAME

DATE OF BIRTH

CHILDREN

NAMES OF OTHER SIBLINGS

YOUR PARTNER'S PATERNAL GRANDMOTHER

Significant details

NAME & NICKNAMES

DATE & PLACE OF BIRTH

DISTINGUISHING PHYSICAL FEATURES

FAMILY CHARACTERISTICS

PHOTOGRAPH

Childhood

CHILDHOOD HOME

FAVOURITE ACTIVITIES

MEMORIES OF PARENTS

MEMORIES OF SCHOOL

Adulthood

FURTHER EDUCATION

FIRST JOB

FIRST PAY PACKET

FIRST MEETING WITH YOUR PARTNER'S GRANDFATHER

FIRST IMPRESSION OF HIM

FIRST HOME

FAVOURITE HOBBIES & PASTIMES

MEMORABLE JOURNEYS & EVENTS

Her brothers & sisters

NAME

DATE OF BIRTH

CHILDREN

NAME

DATE OF BIRTH

CHILDREN

NAME

DATE OF BIRTH

CHILDREN

NAME

DATE OF BIRTH

CHILDREN

NAMES OF OTHER SIBLINGS

Your Partner's Paternal Grandfather

Significant details

NAME & NICKNAMES

DATE & PLACE OF BIRTH

DISTINGUISHING PHYSICAL FEATURES

TYPICAL FAMILY CHARACTERISTICS

Childhood

CHILDHOOD HOME

FAVOURITE ACTIVITIES

MEMORIES OF PARENTS

MEMORIES OF SCHOOL

PHOTOGRAPH

Adulthood

FURTHER EDUCATION

FIRST JOB

FIRST PAY PACKET

WHEN & HOW HE PROPOSED

FIRST IMPRESSION OF YOUR PARTNER'S GRANDMOTHER

HONEYMOON MEMORIES

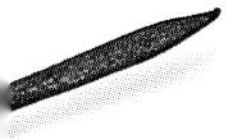

GRANDPARENTS' HOME YOUR PARTNER REMEMBERS

FAVOURITE PASTIMES & HOBBIES

MEMORABLE TRAVEL

His brothers & sisters

NAME

DATE OF BIRTH

CHILDREN

NAME

DATE OF BIRTH

CHILDREN

NAME

DATE OF BIRTH

CHILDREN

NAME

DATE OF BIRTH

CHILDREN

NAMES OF OTHER SIBLINGS

YOUR PARTNER'S GREAT-GRANDPARENTS

Maternal grandmother's mother

NAME

DATE & PLACE OF BIRTH

WHEN & WHERE MARRIED

PHOTOGRAPH

Maternal grandfather's mother

NAME

DATE & PLACE OF BIRTH

WHEN & WHERE MARRIED

PHOTOGRAPH

Maternal grandmother's father

NAME

DATE & PLACE OF BIRTH

HONEYMOON MEMORIES

PHOTOGRAPH

Maternal grandfather's father

NAME

DATE & PLACE OF BIRTH

HONEYMOON MEMORIES

PHOTOGRAPH

Paternal grandmother's mother

NAME

DATE & PLACE OF BIRTH

WHEN & WHERE MARRIED

PHOTOGRAPH

Paternal grandfather's mother

NAME

DATE & PLACE OF BIRTH

WHEN & WHERE MARRIED

PHOTOGRAPH

Paternal grandmother's father

NAME

DATE & PLACE OF BIRTH

HONEYMOON MEMORIES

PHOTOGRAPH

Paternal grandfather's father

NAME

DATE & PLACE OF BIRTH

HONEYMOON MEMORIES

PHOTOGRAPH

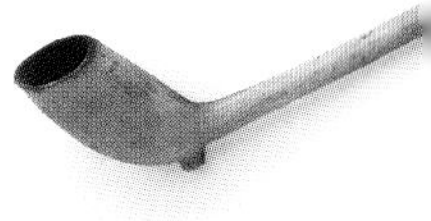

YOUR PARTNER'S OTHER ANCESTORS

Mother's ancestors

NAME

DATE & PLACE OF BIRTH

HOW RELATED

DATE OF DEATH

WHERE BURIED

PHOTOGRAPH

NAME

DATE & PLACE OF BIRTH

HOW RELATED

DATE OF DEATH

WHERE BURIED

HOW THEY WERE TRACED

NAME

DATE & PLACE OF BIRTH

HOW RELATED

DATE OF DEATH

WHERE BURIED

STORIES ABOUT THEM

CHARACTERISTICS PASSED ON TO YOUR PARTNER

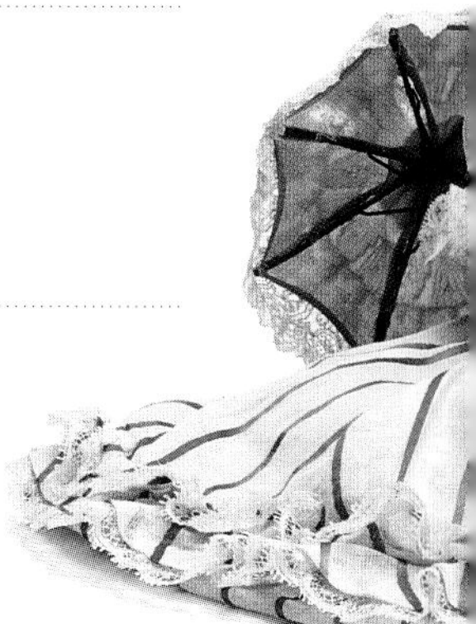

Father's ancestors

NAME

DATE & PLACE OF BIRTH

HOW RELATED

DATE OF DEATH

WHERE BURIED

PHOTOGRAPH

NAME

DATE & PLACE OF BIRTH

HOW RELATED

DATE OF DEATH

WHERE BURIED

NAME

DATE & PLACE OF BIRTH

HOW RELATED

DATE OF DEATH

WHERE BURIED

PHOTOGRAPH

HOW THEY WERE TRACED

STORIES ABOUT THEM

CHARACTERISTICS PASSED ON TO YOUR PARTNER

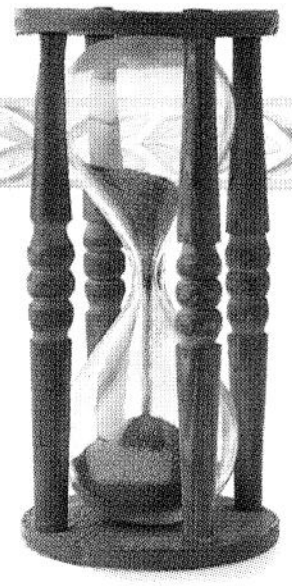

FAMILY STORIES & ANECDOTES

STORIES ABOUT YOUR PARTNER

STORIES ABOUT YOUR PARTNER'S SIBLINGS

ANECDOTES ABOUT FAMILY OCCASIONS

ANECDOTES ABOUT FAMILY HOLIDAYS

ANECDOTES ABOUT FAMILY PETS

PHOTOGRAPH

STORIES ABOUT FATHER

PHOTOGRAPH

STORIES ABOUT GRANDPARENTS

PHOTOGRAPH

STORIES ABOUT MOTHER

STORIES ABOUT GREAT-GRANDPARENTS

STORIES ABOUT AUNTS & UNCLES

FAMILY JOKES

*F*AMILY *T*REE

When you have gathered all the information you need, and have completed your research, write the names of your partner's family members – generation by generation – in the intertwining branches of the tree. This will create a beautiful and lasting visual reminder of his family history to pass on to your children.

FAMILY PHOTOGRAPH

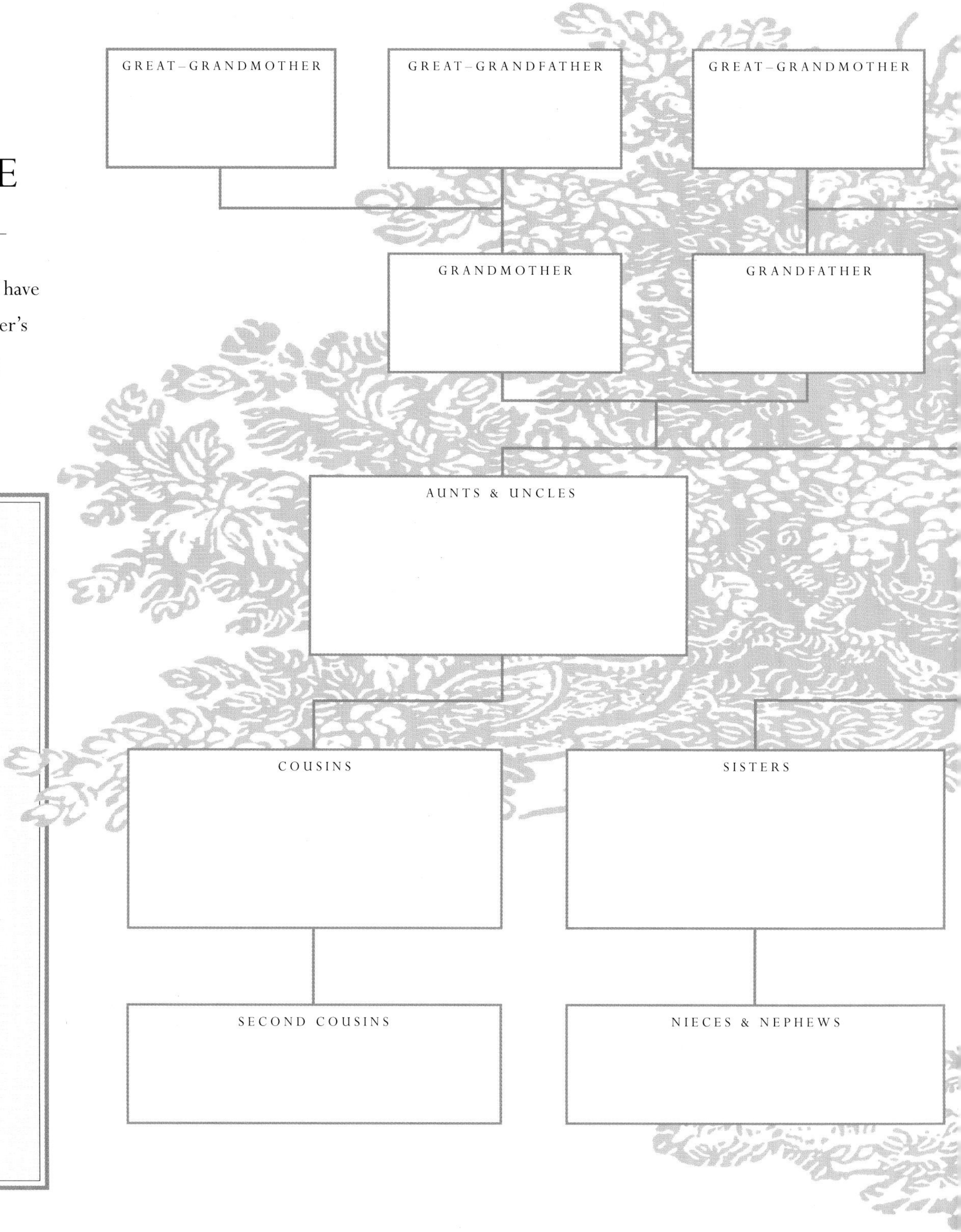